Practice Your Facts
Workbook Level Two

Creative Publications
A Tribune Education Company

Acknowledgments

Project Coordinator Janet Pittock

Design Director Karen Lee

Cover Design Gerta Sorensen

Designer Lynn Capen

Illustrator Susan Aiello Studio

Production Carlisle Communications, Ltd.

Manufacturing Dallas Richards

ISBN 0-7622-1216-0

1 2 3 4 5 6 7 8 ML 05 04 03 02 01 00 99

Catalog No. 32321

Customer Service 800-624-0822

http://www.creativepublications.com

Contents

Introduction

Mastering addition, subtraction, and multiplication facts provides children with basic tools that will enhance their success in mathematics. This book provides straightforward practice for achieving fast recall of the facts.

Overview

The book is organized in a way that allows children to focus on specific groups of facts before proceeding to mixed fact practice. The following summary lists strategies that children are encouraged to use.

Summary of Fact Strategies

Addition: Count on

Counting on zero, one, two, or three is an easy addition strategy to begin with. First children discover and use the simple rules for adding zero or one. Counting on two or three comes next. The count-on strategy covers 72 of the 121 addition facts.

Addition: Doubles

Most children naturally remember doubles. Seeing pictures of doubles helps children remember these facts.

Addition: Near Doubles

Children combine knowledge of doubles facts with the count-on or count-back strategies. When children recognize that addends are only one or two numbers apart, they can find the double of the lesser addend and then count on to find the sum. Conversely, they can find the double of the greater addend and then count back to find the sum. There are thirty-eight near-doubles facts.

Addition: Using Ten

Several strategies relate to the structure of the base-ten number system. These strategies include recognizing pair of addends that equal ten $(6 + 4)$, adding ten to a single-digit addend $(7 + 10 = 17)$, decomposing an addend to create combinations that equal ten $(7 + 8 = 5 + (2 + 8) = 15)$, and finding the difference between numbers and ten $(12 - 7 = (12 - 10) + (10 - 7) = 2 + 3 = 5)$.

Subtraction: Count up

In using the count-up strategy to subtract, children begin with the lesser number and then count up to the greater number, keeping track of how many numbers they count. For example, for $11 - 9$, children begin at 9 and count 10, 11. Two numbers were counted, so $11 - 9 = 2$.

Subtraction: Count back

The count-back strategy is one that many children naturally use to subtract. They quickly discover and use the simple rules for subtracting zero or one. Children extend this strategy to subtract two or three.

Subtraction: Think Addition

Many children naturally think of related addition facts when they subtract. For example, for $13 - 8$, children solve what plus 8 equals 13.

Multiplication: Zero, One, and Ten Rules

The zero, one, and ten rules strategy uses patterns produced by properties of the base ten system. Zero times anything is zero. One times any number is that number. Ten times any number moves the number one decimal place to the left.

Multiplication: Doubles and Five-0s

Numbers multiplied by two have the same result as the doubles addition fact for that number. The product of any number times five ends in five or zero. Nearly every child learns to count by fives and recognizes this pattern.

$$\xleftarrow{\hspace{1cm}} 0 \quad 1 \quad 2 \quad 3 \quad 4 \quad 5 \quad 6 \quad 7 \quad 8 \quad 9 \quad 10 \quad 11 \quad 12 \xrightarrow{\hspace{1cm}}$$

Use the number line to add.
Count on 0, 1, or 2.

1 $7 + 1 =$ ____ $5 + 1 =$ ____ $3 + 0 =$ ____

2 $6 + 2 =$ ____ $4 + 2 =$ ____ $8 + 0 =$ ____

3 $4 + 0 =$ ____ $7 + 0 =$ ____ $2 + 1 =$ ____

4
$$\begin{array}{r} 7 \\ + 2 \\ \hline \end{array} \qquad \begin{array}{r} 5 \\ + 0 \\ \hline \end{array} \qquad \begin{array}{r} 9 \\ + 2 \\ \hline \end{array} \qquad \begin{array}{r} 6 \\ + 1 \\ \hline \end{array} \qquad \begin{array}{r} 1 \\ + 0 \\ \hline \end{array}$$

5
$$\begin{array}{r} 8 \\ + 1 \\ \hline \end{array} \qquad \begin{array}{r} 9 \\ + 0 \\ \hline \end{array} \qquad \begin{array}{r} 2 \\ + 2 \\ \hline \end{array} \qquad \begin{array}{r} 10 \\ + 0 \\ \hline \end{array} \qquad \begin{array}{r} 3 \\ + 1 \\ \hline \end{array}$$

6
$$\begin{array}{r} 4 \\ + 1 \\ \hline \end{array} \qquad \begin{array}{r} 5 \\ + 2 \\ \hline \end{array} \qquad \begin{array}{r} 6 \\ + 0 \\ \hline \end{array} \qquad \begin{array}{r} 2 \\ + 0 \\ \hline \end{array} \qquad \begin{array}{r} 9 \\ + 1 \\ \hline \end{array}$$

Add. Count on 0, 1, or 2.

1 ⑤ ● ●

5 + 2 = ____

● ⑧

1 + 8 = ____

2 ⑥ ●

6 + 1 = ____

⑦ ● ●

7 + 2 = ____

3 ④ ● ●

4 + 2 = ____

⑨

0 + 9 = ____

4
$$\begin{array}{r}0\\+4\\\hline\end{array}\qquad\begin{array}{r}8\\+2\\\hline\end{array}\qquad\begin{array}{r}0\\+1\\\hline\end{array}\qquad\begin{array}{r}6\\+2\\\hline\end{array}\qquad\begin{array}{r}7\\+1\\\hline\end{array}$$

5
$$\begin{array}{r}2\\+0\\\hline\end{array}\qquad\begin{array}{r}1\\+4\\\hline\end{array}\qquad\begin{array}{r}0\\+8\\\hline\end{array}\qquad\begin{array}{r}5\\+0\\\hline\end{array}\qquad\begin{array}{r}1\\+2\\\hline\end{array}$$

6
$$\begin{array}{r}1\\+3\\\hline\end{array}\qquad\begin{array}{r}9\\+2\\\hline\end{array}\qquad\begin{array}{r}0\\+7\\\hline\end{array}\qquad\begin{array}{r}9\\+1\\\hline\end{array}\qquad\begin{array}{r}3\\+2\\\hline\end{array}$$

Count on 0, 1, 2, or 3.

1
7	2	1	3	7
+ 3	+ 9	+ 4	+ 0	+ 1

2
2	3	4	3	6
+ 8	+ 5	+ 3	+ 8	+ 3

3
3	8	9	8	9
+ 9	+ 2	+ 3	+ 3	+ 0

Add to complete. Look for patterns.

4

+	1
3	4
4	
5	
6	

+	2
9	
8	
7	
6	

+	3
3	
4	
5	
6	

Name _____

Add.
Match the sum to a color.
Color the space.

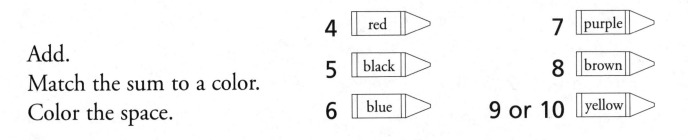

4 | red
5 | black
6 | blue
7 | purple
8 | brown
9 or 10 | yellow

9 +0	3 +7	5 +1	4 +2	3 +6	9 +1
1 +8	3 +1	4 + 3 = ___		2 +2	10 +0
		3 + 3 = ___			
2 +8	5 +3	1 + 6 = ___		6 +2	8 +1
		6 + 0 = ___			
7 +2	0 +4			1 +3	0 +9
		6 + 3 = ___			
3 + 2 = ___	2 + 7 = ___		4 + 1 = ___		

Write the doubles fact. Draw another dot.
Write the doubles-plus-1 fact.

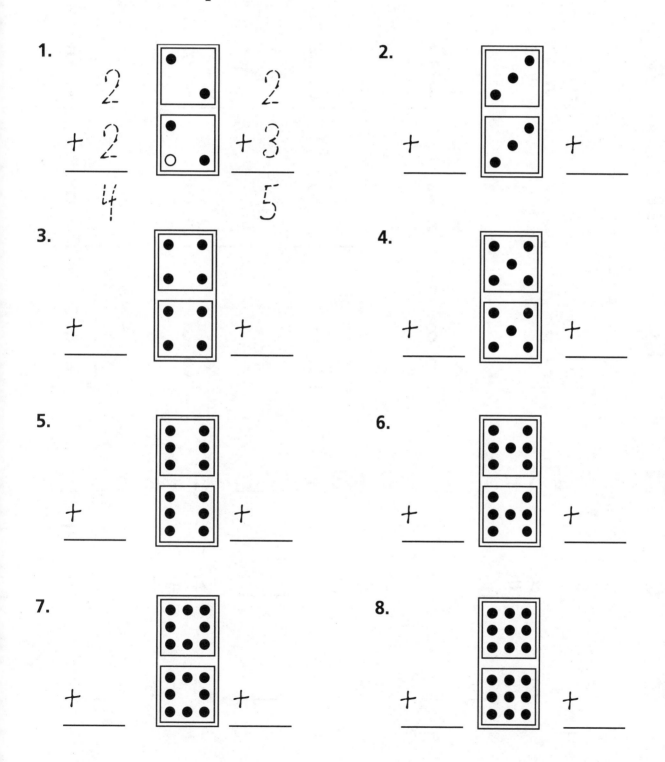

1.

$$\begin{array}{r} 2 \\ +\ 2 \\ \hline 4 \end{array}$$

$$\begin{array}{r} 2 \\ +\ 3 \\ \hline 5 \end{array}$$

2.

$+$ _____ $+$ _____

3.

$+$ _____ $+$ _____

4.

$+$ _____ $+$ _____

5.

$+$ _____ $+$ _____

6.

$+$ _____ $+$ _____

7.

$+$ _____ $+$ _____

8.

$+$ _____ $+$ _____

Add.
Remember to count on from doubles.

1

6	2	4	8	5
+ 5	+ 1	+ 3	+ 7	+ 7

2

7	7	2	8	6
+ 9	+ 5	+ 4	+ 10	+ 7

3

3	8	5	5	6
+ 2	+ 9	+ 4	+ 3	+ 4

4   7 + 6 = _____   2 + 3 = _____   4 + 2 = _____

5   6 + 8 = _____   7 + 8 = _____   4 + 5 = _____

6   9 + 8 = _____   10 + 9 = _____   4 + 6 = _____

Add across and down.

1. $3 + 3 =$ ⬚
$\underline{+\ 6}$

2. $3 + 2 =$ ⬚
$\underline{+\ 5}$
⬚ $+ 9 =$ _____

3. $3 + 4 =$ ⬚
$\underline{+\ 7}$

4. $2 + 1 =$ ⬚
$\underline{+\ 3}$
⬚ $+ 5 =$ _____

5. $4 + 5 =$ ⬚
$\underline{+\ 9}$

6. $4 + 2 =$ ⬚
$\underline{+\ 4}$
⬚ $+ 8 =$ _____

7. $5 + 3 =$ ⬚
$\underline{+\ 9}$

8. $2 + 2 =$ ⬚
$\underline{+\ 3}$
⬚ $+ 8 =$ _____

Add. Find the sum in the table.
Write the letter for the sum.

How do you use doubles to find near doubles?

$$\begin{array}{r} 5 \\ + 4 \\ \hline \square \end{array} \qquad \begin{array}{r} 6 \\ + 7 \\ \hline \square \end{array} \qquad \begin{array}{r} 9 \\ + 8 \\ \hline \square \end{array} \qquad \begin{array}{r} 8 \\ + 8 \\ \hline \square \end{array} \qquad \begin{array}{r} 8 \\ + 7 \\ \hline \square \end{array}$$

$$\begin{array}{r} 5 \\ + 6 \\ \hline \square \end{array} \qquad \begin{array}{r} 6 \\ + 6 \\ \hline \square \end{array} \qquad \begin{array}{r} 7 \\ + 6 \\ \hline \square \end{array} \qquad \begin{array}{r} 9 \\ + 7 \\ \hline \square \end{array} \qquad \begin{array}{r} 5 \\ + 5 \\ \hline \square \end{array}$$

$$\begin{array}{r} 5 \\ + 3 \\ \hline \square \end{array} \qquad \begin{array}{r} 7 \\ + 7 \\ \hline \square \end{array} \qquad \begin{array}{r} 7 \\ + 8 \\ \hline \square \end{array} \qquad \begin{array}{r} 9 \\ + 9 \\ \hline \square \end{array} \qquad \begin{array}{r} 6 \\ + 5 \\ \hline \square \end{array}$$

O	C	E	O	N	O	R	T	N	U	W
8	9	10	11	12	13	14	15	16	17	18

Use the ten-frame to find all the sums of ten.
Write the sum.

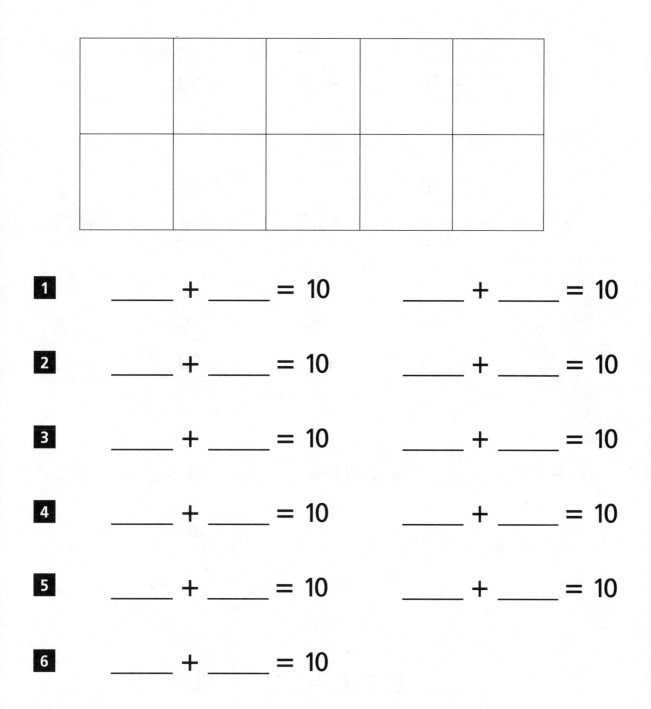

1 ____ + ____ = 10   ____ + ____ = 10

2 ____ + ____ = 10   ____ + ____ = 10

3 ____ + ____ = 10   ____ + ____ = 10

4 ____ + ____ = 10   ____ + ____ = 10

5 ____ + ____ = 10   ____ + ____ = 10

6 ____ + ____ = 10

Add 10.
Remember to think about tens and ones.

1

4 + 10	5 + 10	10 + 2	6 + 10	10 + 9

2

10 + 7	10 + 0	1 + 10	10 + 6	3 + 10

3

2 + 10	10 + 4	10 + 5	9 + 10	8 + 10

4 7 + 10 = _____   5 + 10 = _____   10 + 3 = _____

5 4 + 10 = _____   10 + 8 = _____   6 + 10 = _____

6 10 + 9 = _____   0 + 10 = _____   10 + 1 = _____

Add.

1

4	0	5	8	2
+ 6	+ 10	+ 5	+ 10	+ 8

2

6	7	10	10	9
+ 10	+ 3	+ 1	+ 5	+ 1

3

10	3	10	4	10
+ 9	+ 7	+ 3	+ 10	+ 2

4 $1 + 9 =$ _____ $10 + 7 =$ _____ $10 + 8 =$ _____

5 $8 + 2 =$ _____ $6 + 4 =$ _____ $10 + 2 =$ _____

6 $1 + 10 =$ _____ $10 + 6 =$ _____ $9 + 10 =$ _____

Add. Draw lines to match facts that have the same sums.

A

1 + 10 = 11   Ⓐ

4 + 10 = ____   Ⓑ

10 + 2 = ____   Ⓒ

7 + 10 = ____   Ⓓ

8 + 10 = ____   Ⓔ

3 + 10 = ____   Ⓕ

10 + 9 = ____   Ⓖ

10 + 5 = ____   Ⓗ

3 + 7 = ____   Ⓘ

10 + 6 = ____   Ⓙ

B

① 7 + 3 = ____

② 9 + 10 = ____

③ 5 + 10 = ____

④ 10 + 4 = ____

⑤ 10 + 1 = 11

⑥ 2 + 10 = ____

⑦ 10 + 8 = ____

⑧ 10 + 3 = ____

⑨ 6 + 10 = ____

⑩ 10 + 7 = ____

Use counters and the ten-frame.
Write the sum.

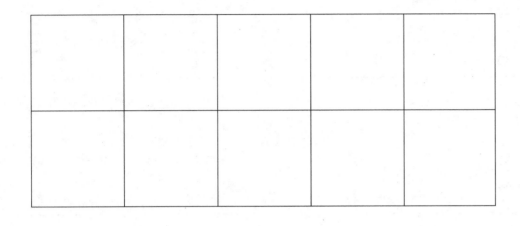

1 7 + 5	4 + 9	9 + 6	8 + 4
2 5 + 9	6 + 8	3 + 9	5 + 8
3 7 + 4	8 + 7	6 + 5	7 + 9

Use counters and a ten-frame.
Write the sum.

1

7	4	5	8
+ 6	+ 9	+ 6	+ 3

2

9	6	5	4
+ 7	+ 8	+ 9	+ 8

3

6	5	8	7
+ 9	+ 8	+ 9	+ 5

Color beads to show the top number in each fact.
Use a different color to show the bottom number.
Ring 10 beads. Write the sum.

1.   9   ●●●●●●●●●○
    + 7   ○○○○○○○○○○

    16

2.   5   ○○○○○○○○○○
    + 8   ○○○○○○○○○○

3.   6   ○○○○○○○○○○
    + 9   ○○○○○○○○○○

4.   8   ○○○○○○○○○○
    + 4   ○○○○○○○○○○

5.   7   ○○○○○○○○○○
    + 5   ○○○○○○○○○○

6.   3   ○○○○○○○○○○
    + 9   ○○○○○○○○○○

7.   8   ○○○○○○○○○○
    + 7   ○○○○○○○○○○

8.   9   ○○○○○○○○○○
    + 5   ○○○○○○○○○○

Look for patterns.
Write the sum.

1
$$\begin{array}{r} 5 \\ + 5 \\ \hline \end{array}$$
$$\begin{array}{r} 5 \\ + 6 \\ \hline \end{array}$$
$$\begin{array}{r} 5 \\ + 7 \\ \hline \end{array}$$
$$\begin{array}{r} 5 \\ + 8 \\ \hline \end{array}$$

2
$$\begin{array}{r} 6 \\ + 5 \\ \hline \end{array}$$
$$\begin{array}{r} 6 \\ + 6 \\ \hline \end{array}$$
$$\begin{array}{r} 6 \\ + 7 \\ \hline \end{array}$$
$$\begin{array}{r} 6 \\ + 8 \\ \hline \end{array}$$

3
$$\begin{array}{r} 7 \\ + 6 \\ \hline \end{array}$$
$$\begin{array}{r} 7 \\ + 7 \\ \hline \end{array}$$
$$\begin{array}{r} 7 \\ + 8 \\ \hline \end{array}$$
$$\begin{array}{r} 7 \\ + 9 \\ \hline \end{array}$$

4
$$\begin{array}{r} 8 \\ + 6 \\ \hline \end{array}$$
$$\begin{array}{r} 8 \\ + 7 \\ \hline \end{array}$$
$$\begin{array}{r} 8 \\ + 8 \\ \hline \end{array}$$
$$\begin{array}{r} 8 \\ + 9 \\ \hline \end{array}$$

5
$$\begin{array}{r} 9 \\ + 6 \\ \hline \end{array}$$
$$\begin{array}{r} 9 \\ + 7 \\ \hline \end{array}$$
$$\begin{array}{r} 9 \\ + 8 \\ \hline \end{array}$$
$$\begin{array}{r} 9 \\ + 9 \\ \hline \end{array}$$

Add. Write the sum.

1

$$\begin{array}{r} 5 \\ + 6 \\ \hline \end{array}$$
$$\begin{array}{r} 8 \\ + 3 \\ \hline \end{array}$$
$$\begin{array}{r} 4 \\ + 8 \\ \hline \end{array}$$
$$\begin{array}{r} 9 \\ + 5 \\ \hline \end{array}$$

2

$$\begin{array}{r} 6 \\ + 8 \\ \hline \end{array}$$
$$\begin{array}{r} 9 \\ + 7 \\ \hline \end{array}$$
$$\begin{array}{r} 6 \\ + 8 \\ \hline \end{array}$$
$$\begin{array}{r} 7 \\ + 6 \\ \hline \end{array}$$

3

$$\begin{array}{r} 5 \\ + 7 \\ \hline \end{array}$$
$$\begin{array}{r} 7 \\ + 8 \\ \hline \end{array}$$
$$\begin{array}{r} 7 \\ + 9 \\ \hline \end{array}$$
$$\begin{array}{r} 8 \\ + 6 \\ \hline \end{array}$$

4

$$\begin{array}{r} 8 \\ + 7 \\ \hline \end{array}$$
$$\begin{array}{r} 8 \\ + 4 \\ \hline \end{array}$$
$$\begin{array}{r} 8 \\ + 9 \\ \hline \end{array}$$
$$\begin{array}{r} 9 \\ + 6 \\ \hline \end{array}$$

5

$$\begin{array}{r} 3 \\ + 8 \\ \hline \end{array}$$
$$\begin{array}{r} 9 \\ + 8 \\ \hline \end{array}$$
$$\begin{array}{r} 5 \\ + 9 \\ \hline \end{array}$$
$$\begin{array}{r} 8 \\ + 5 \\ \hline \end{array}$$

Add.

1

$$\begin{array}{r} 5 \\ + 6 \\ \hline \end{array}$$
$$\begin{array}{r} 2 \\ + 9 \\ \hline \end{array}$$
$$\begin{array}{r} 7 \\ + 7 \\ \hline \end{array}$$
$$\begin{array}{r} 8 \\ + 3 \\ \hline \end{array}$$
$$\begin{array}{r} 6 \\ + 6 \\ \hline \end{array}$$

2

$$\begin{array}{r} 7 \\ + 9 \\ \hline \end{array}$$
$$\begin{array}{r} 6 \\ + 7 \\ \hline \end{array}$$
$$\begin{array}{r} 8 \\ + 8 \\ \hline \end{array}$$
$$\begin{array}{r} 8 \\ + 4 \\ \hline \end{array}$$
$$\begin{array}{r} 5 \\ + 9 \\ \hline \end{array}$$

3

$$\begin{array}{r} 7 \\ + 4 \\ \hline \end{array}$$
$$\begin{array}{r} 9 \\ + 4 \\ \hline \end{array}$$
$$\begin{array}{r} 7 \\ + 8 \\ \hline \end{array}$$
$$\begin{array}{r} 5 \\ + 7 \\ \hline \end{array}$$
$$\begin{array}{r} 8 \\ + 6 \\ \hline \end{array}$$

4   3 + 9 = _____   9 + 6 = _____   6 + 8 = _____

5   5 + 8 = _____   8 + 7 = _____   9 + 3 = _____

6   8 + 9 = _____   9 + 9 = _____   7 + 6 = _____

Add. Write the sum.

1 6 + 2 = _____   5 + 5 = _____   4 + 1 = _____

2 8 + 3 = _____   0 + 7 = _____   9 + 5 = _____

3 3 + 6 = _____   1 + 10 = _____   2 + 4 = _____

4 7 + 5 = _____   4 + 8 = _____   7 + 7 = _____

5 5 + 2 = _____   10 + 3 = _____   7 + 2 = _____

6 8 + 9 = _____   6 + 0 = _____   9 + 4 = _____

Add. Write the sum.

1 1 + 5	4 + 6	10 + 0	7 + 1
2 3 + 9	2 + 6	9 + 2	5 + 4
3 6 + 7	8 + 8	0 + 6	2 + 3
4 10 + 4	3 + 7	1 + 2	8 + 0
5 9 + 7	4 + 5	5 + 10	6 + 3

Add. Write the sum.

1

$$7 + 8 = \underline{\hspace{1cm}}$$
$$4 + 2 = \underline{\hspace{1cm}}$$
$$3 + 5 = \underline{\hspace{1cm}}$$
$$2 + 9 = \underline{\hspace{1cm}}$$

2

$$0 + 4 = \underline{\hspace{1cm}}$$
$$10 + 7 = \underline{\hspace{1cm}}$$
$$8 + 4 = \underline{\hspace{1cm}}$$
$$9 + 6 = \underline{\hspace{1cm}}$$

3

$$5 + 0 = \underline{\hspace{1cm}}$$
$$1 + 1 = \underline{\hspace{1cm}}$$
$$6 + 5 = \underline{\hspace{1cm}}$$
$$8 + 1 = \underline{\hspace{1cm}}$$

4   2 + 2 = _____   7 + 3 = _____   4 + 9 = _____

5   0 + 10 = _____   9 + 3 = _____   5 + 8 = _____

6   1 + 4 = _____   10 + 6 = _____   7 + 9 = _____

Find each sum.

1 9 + 2 = _____   7 + 7 = _____   8 + 6 = _____

2 4 + 8 = _____   6 + 3 = _____   7 + 6 = _____

3 8 + 2 = _____   5 + 8 = _____   3 + 8 = _____

4 9 + 4 = _____   6 + 5 = _____   6 + 4 = _____

5 4 + 5 = _____   3 + 9 = _____   7 + 2 = _____

6 9 + 5 = _____   7 + 3 = _____   7 + 5 = _____

Add. Write the sum.

1 $8 + 2 =$ _____ $3 + 3 =$ _____ $4 + 10 =$ _____

2 $7 + 6 =$ _____ $5 + 2 =$ _____ $0 + 2 =$ _____

3 $1 + 7 =$ _____ $6 + 4 =$ _____ $10 + 5 =$ _____

4 $9 + 0 =$ _____ $2 + 7 =$ _____ $3 + 8 =$ _____

5 $9 + 1 =$ _____ $10 + 0 =$ _____ $6 + 6 =$ _____

6 $4 + 3 =$ _____ $0 + 1 =$ _____ $7 + 4 =$ _____

Add. Write the sum.

1

8	3	4	1
+ 7	+ 0	+ 4	+ 9

2

0	2	9	5
+ 5	+ 8	+ 10	+ 6

3

6	10	7	8
+ 1	+ 2	+ 9	+ 5

4

0	2	3	4
+ 0	+ 1	+ 4	+ 7

5

10	6	1	9
+ 1	+ 8	+ 3	+ 9

Add. Write the sum.

1   5 + 7 = _____   7 + 10 = _____   8 + 6 = _____

2   0 + 9 = _____   4 + 0 = _____   3 + 2 = _____

3   10 + 9 = _____   2 + 10 = _____   1 + 0 = _____

4

$$\begin{array}{r} 6 \\ +\ 9 \\ \hline \end{array} \qquad \begin{array}{r} 9 \\ +\ 8 \\ \hline \end{array} \qquad \begin{array}{r} 3 \\ +\ 10 \\ \hline \end{array} \qquad \begin{array}{r} 2 \\ +\ 5 \\ \hline \end{array}$$

5

$$\begin{array}{r} 5 \\ +\ 3 \\ \hline \end{array} \qquad \begin{array}{r} 10 \\ +\ 10 \\ \hline \end{array} \qquad \begin{array}{r} 0 \\ +\ 8 \\ \hline \end{array} \qquad \begin{array}{r} 7 \\ +\ 0 \\ \hline \end{array}$$

6

$$\begin{array}{r} 6 \\ +\ 10 \\ \hline \end{array} \qquad \begin{array}{r} 1 \\ +\ 8 \\ \hline \end{array} \qquad \begin{array}{r} 2 \\ +\ 0 \\ \hline \end{array} \qquad \begin{array}{r} 7 \\ +\ 8 \\ \hline \end{array}$$

Add. Write the sum.

1	10 + 5	7 + 7	8 + 9	1 + 5	9 + 9
2	8 + 5	5 + 6	2 + 3	1 + 1	10 + 7
3	2 + 0	8 + 2	4 + 10	7 + 6	1 + 2
4	8 + 10	6 + 8	4 + 1	8 + 8	3 + 10
5	4 + 4	9 + 4	7 + 5	6 + 6	4 + 3

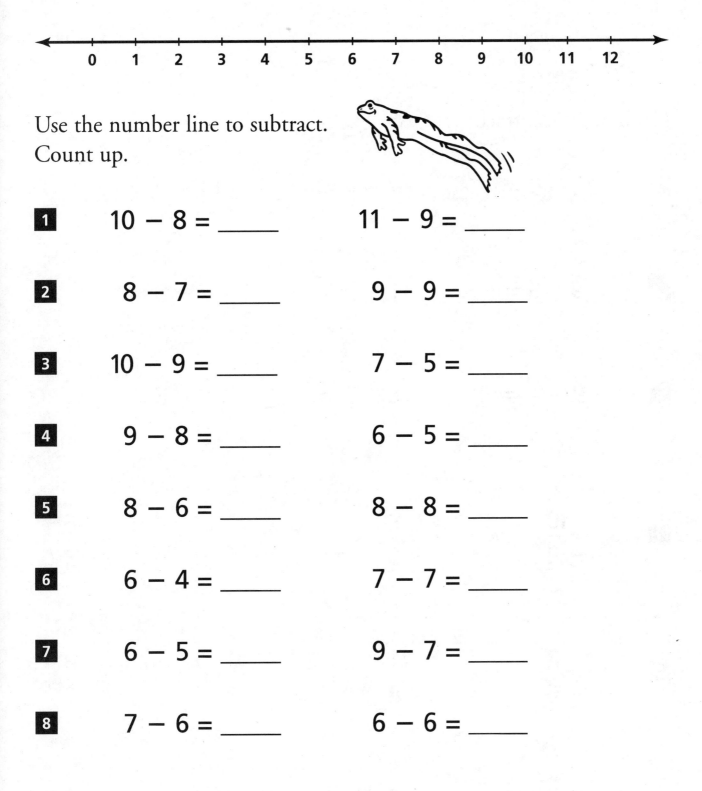

Use the number line to subtract.
Count up.

1   10 − 8 = ____   11 − 9 = ____

2   8 − 7 = ____   9 − 9 = ____

3   10 − 9 = ____   7 − 5 = ____

4   9 − 8 = ____   6 − 5 = ____

5   8 − 6 = ____   8 − 8 = ____

6   6 − 4 = ____   7 − 7 = ____

7   6 − 5 = ____   9 − 7 = ____

8   7 − 6 = ____   6 − 6 = ____

$$0 \quad 1 \quad 2 \quad 3 \quad 4 \quad 5 \quad 6 \quad 7 \quad 8 \quad 9 \quad 10 \quad 11 \quad 12$$

Count up to subtract.

1 $12 - 9 = $ _____ $7 - 4 = $ _____ $10 - 9 = $ _____

2 $9 - 8 = $ _____ $11 - 9 = $ _____ $7 - 5 = $ _____

3 $9 - 9 = $ _____ $8 - 7 = $ _____ $9 - 6 = $ _____

4
$$\begin{array}{r} 10 \\ -8 \\ \hline \end{array} \qquad \begin{array}{r} 8 \\ -5 \\ \hline \end{array} \qquad \begin{array}{r} 7 \\ -7 \\ \hline \end{array} \qquad \begin{array}{r} 6 \\ -3 \\ \hline \end{array}$$

5
$$\begin{array}{r} 8 \\ -6 \\ \hline \end{array} \qquad \begin{array}{r} 11 \\ -8 \\ \hline \end{array} \qquad \begin{array}{r} 10 \\ -7 \\ \hline \end{array} \qquad \begin{array}{r} 9 \\ -7 \\ \hline \end{array}$$

6
$$\begin{array}{r} 8 \\ -8 \\ \hline \end{array} \qquad \begin{array}{r} 6 \\ -4 \\ \hline \end{array} \qquad \begin{array}{r} 7 \\ -6 \\ \hline \end{array} \qquad \begin{array}{r} 6 \\ -5 \\ \hline \end{array}$$

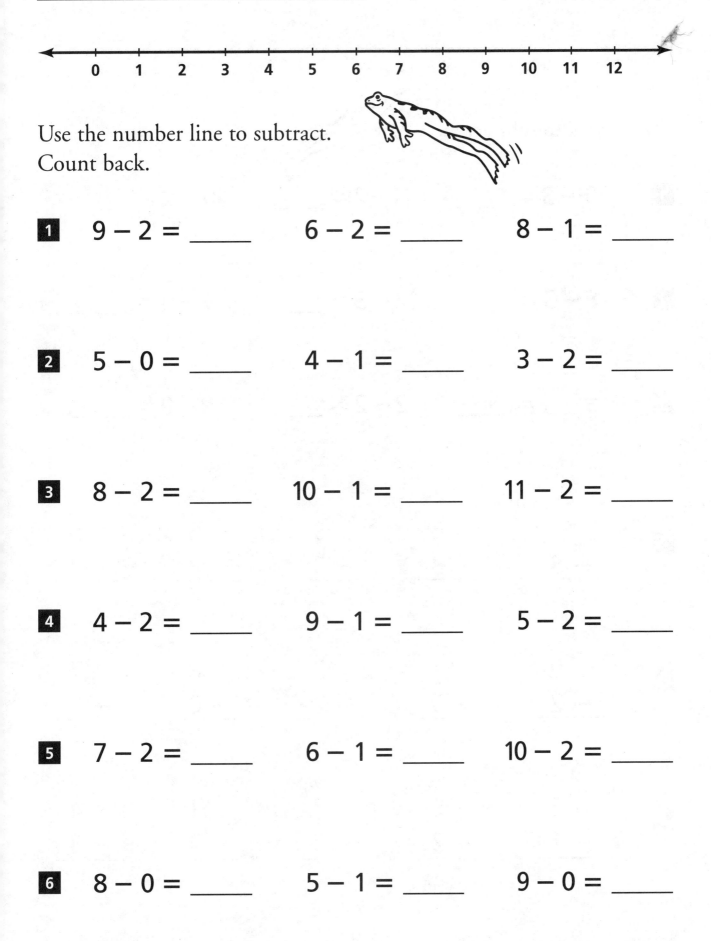

Use the number line to subtract.
Count back.

1 $9 - 2 =$ _____ $6 - 2 =$ _____ $8 - 1 =$ _____

2 $5 - 0 =$ _____ $4 - 1 =$ _____ $3 - 2 =$ _____

3 $8 - 2 =$ _____ $10 - 1 =$ _____ $11 - 2 =$ _____

4 $4 - 2 =$ _____ $9 - 1 =$ _____ $5 - 2 =$ _____

5 $7 - 2 =$ _____ $6 - 1 =$ _____ $10 - 2 =$ _____

6 $8 - 0 =$ _____ $5 - 1 =$ _____ $9 - 0 =$ _____

```
←——┼——┼——┼——┼——┼——┼——┼——┼——┼——┼——┼——┼——┼——→
    0   1   2   3   4   5   6   7   8   9  10  11  12
```

Count back to subtract.

1   9 − 3 = _____   4 − 2 = _____   10 − 2 = _____

2   8 − 3 = _____   12 − 3 = _____   7 − 1 = _____

3   9 − 1 = _____   2 − 2 = _____   9 − 0 = _____

4
```
  10      6      3      6      5
 − 3     − 3    − 3    − 2    − 3
 ────    ────   ────   ────   ────
```

5
```
   9     11      3      8      7
 − 2     − 3    − 2    − 0    − 2
 ────    ────   ────   ────   ────
```

6
```
   5      8      7     11      4
 − 1     − 2    − 3    − 2    − 3
 ────    ────   ────   ────   ────
```

Name _____

Subtract.
Color inside the spaces where half is left.

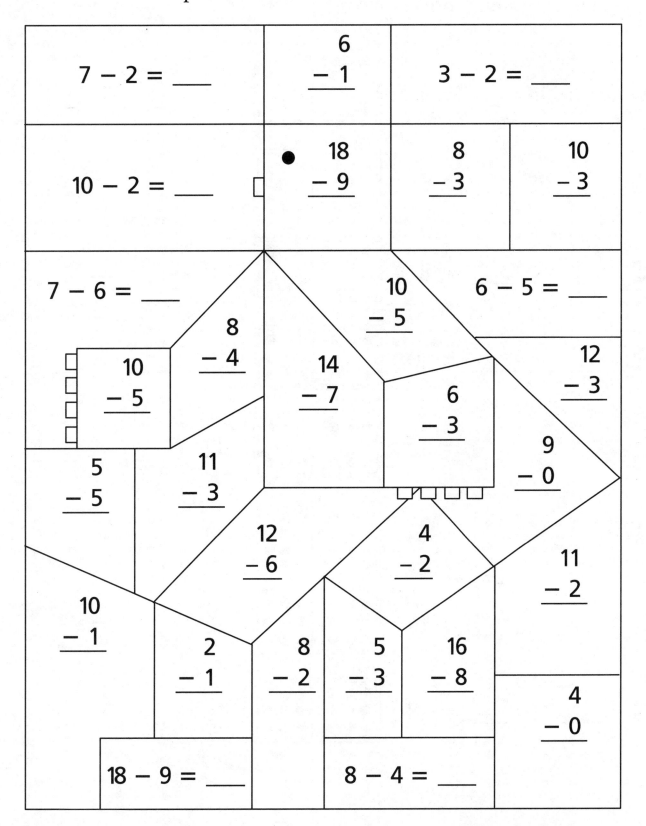

Write addition doubles.
Write the matching subtraction fact.

1 ___ + ___ = 4   4 − ___ = ___

2 ___ + ___ = 6   6 − ___ = ___

3 ___ + ___ = 8   8 − ___ = ___

4 ___ + ___ = 10   10 − ___ = ___

5 ___ + ___ = 12   12 − ___ = ___

6 ___ + ___ = 14   14 − ___ = ___

7 ___ + ___ = 16   16 − ___ = ___

8 ___ + ___ = 18   18 − ___ = ___

Think about sums of 10.
Add or subtract.

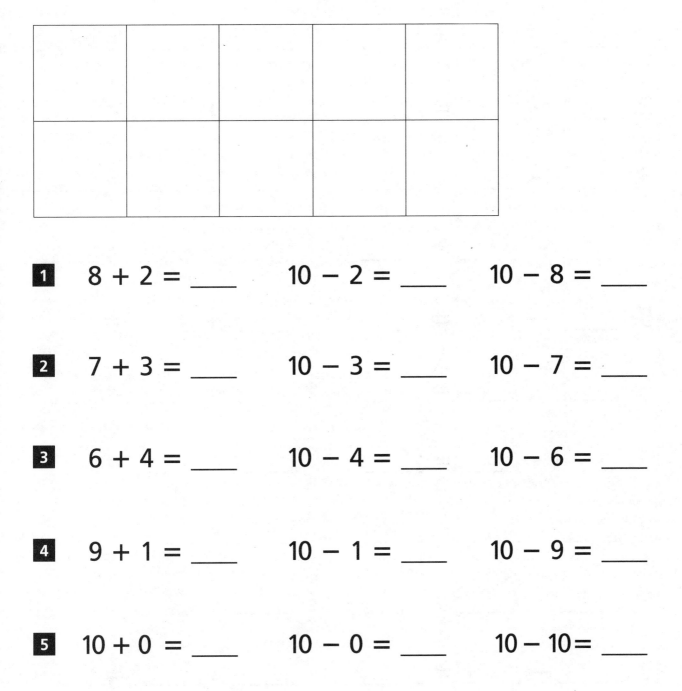

1   8 + 2 = ___   10 − 2 = ___   10 − 8 = ___

2   7 + 3 = ___   10 − 3 = ___   10 − 7 = ___

3   6 + 4 = ___   10 − 4 = ___   10 − 6 = ___

4   9 + 1 = ___   10 − 1 = ___   10 − 9 = ___

5   10 + 0 = ___   10 − 0 = ___   10 − 10 = ___

Snap together 10 cubes.
Break off some cubes.
Write the subtraction.
Make 10 again. Write the addition.

1. _____ − _____ = _____   _____ + _____ = _____

2. _____ − _____ = _____   _____ + _____ = _____

3. _____ − _____ = _____   _____ + _____ = _____

4. _____ − _____ = _____   _____ + _____ = _____

5. _____ − _____ = _____   _____ + _____ = _____

6. _____ − _____ = _____   _____ + _____ = _____

7. _____ − _____ = _____   _____ + _____ = _____

8. _____ − _____ = _____   _____ + _____ = _____

9. _____ − _____ = _____   _____ + _____ = _____

10. _____ − _____ = _____   _____ + _____ = _____

11. _____ − _____ = _____   _____ + _____ = _____

Think of addition facts for 4, 5, or 6.
Find the difference.

1 $10 - 4 =$ _____ $4 +$ _____ $= 10$

2 $7 - 6 =$ _____ $6 +$ _____ $= 7$

3 $13 - 4 =$ _____ $4 +$ _____ $= 13$

4 $9 - 5 =$ _____ $5 +$ _____ $= 9$

5 $13 - 6 =$ _____ $6 +$ _____ $= 13$

6 $11 - 4 =$ _____ $4 +$ _____ $= 11$

7 $12 - 5 =$ _____ $5 +$ _____ $= 12$

8 $8 - 6 =$ _____ $6 +$ _____ $= 8$

9 $14 - 5 =$ _____ $5 +$ _____ $= 14$

10 $11 - 6 =$ _____ $6 +$ _____ $= 11$

11 $12 - 4 =$ _____ $4 +$ _____ $= 12$

Subtract.

1			
7 − 6	9 − 4	15 − 6	8 − 4

2			
10 − 4	8 − 6	12 − 4	14 − 6

3			
8 − 5	12 − 6	9 − 6	13 − 5

4			
11 − 4	10 − 5	14 − 5	7 − 4

5			
13 − 6	13 − 4	12 − 5	11 − 5

Think of addition facts for 7 or 8.
Find the difference.

1 $15 - 7 =$ _____ $7 +$ _____ $= 15$

2 $17 - 8 =$ _____ $8 +$ _____ $= 17$

3 $12 - 7 =$ _____ $7 +$ _____ $= 12$

4 $14 - 8 =$ _____ $8 +$ _____ $= 14$

5 $16 - 7 =$ _____ $7 +$ _____ $= 16$

6 $11 - 8 =$ _____ $8 +$ _____ $= 11$

7 $12 - 8 =$ _____ $8 +$ _____ $= 12$

8 $13 - 7 =$ _____ $7 +$ _____ $= 13$

9 $10 - 8 =$ _____ $8 +$ _____ $= 10$

10 $13 - 8 =$ _____ $8 +$ _____ $= 13$

11 $10 - 7 =$ _____ $7 +$ _____ $= 10$

Subtract.

1
13	15	8	9	11
− 7	− 8	− 7	− 8	− 7

2
16	7	14	12	15
− 7	− 7	− 7	− 7	− 7

3
10	11	17	8	13
− 8	− 8	− 8	− 8	− 8

4
9	14	12	16	10
− 7	− 8	− 8	− 8	− 7

5
9	15	17	16	12
− 8	− 7	− 8	− 7	− 8

Find each difference.
Write the letter on the blank over the differences below.

B. 14 – 9 = _____   D. 17 – 9 = _____

D. 10 – 9 = _____   I 15 – 9 = _____

O. 11 – 9 = _____   R. 18 – 9 = _____

R. 16 – 9 = _____   W. 13 – 9 = _____

Y. 12 – 9 = _____   Y. 9 – 9 = _____

┌───┐
│ What do you call a parrot that talks a lot? │
└───┘

___ ___ ___ ___ ___   ___ ___ ___ ___ ___
 4   2   9   8   3   5   6   7   1   0

Name

$8 \div 4 = 2$

Add. Subtract.
Match related facts.

1   9 + 1 = 10   12 − 9 = 3

2   9 + 2 = 11   16 − 9 = 7

3   9 + 3 = 12   11 − 9 = 2

4   9 + 4 = 13   10 − 9 = 1

5   9 + 5 = 14   14 − 9 = 5

6   9 + 6 = 15   17 − 9 = 8

7   9 + 7 = 16   15 − 9 = 6

8   9 + 8 = 17   18 − 9 = 9

9   9 + 9 = 18   13 − 9 = 4

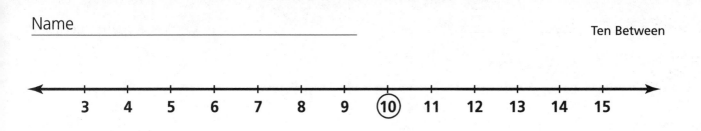

Look to see if 10 is between two numbers in a subtraction fact.

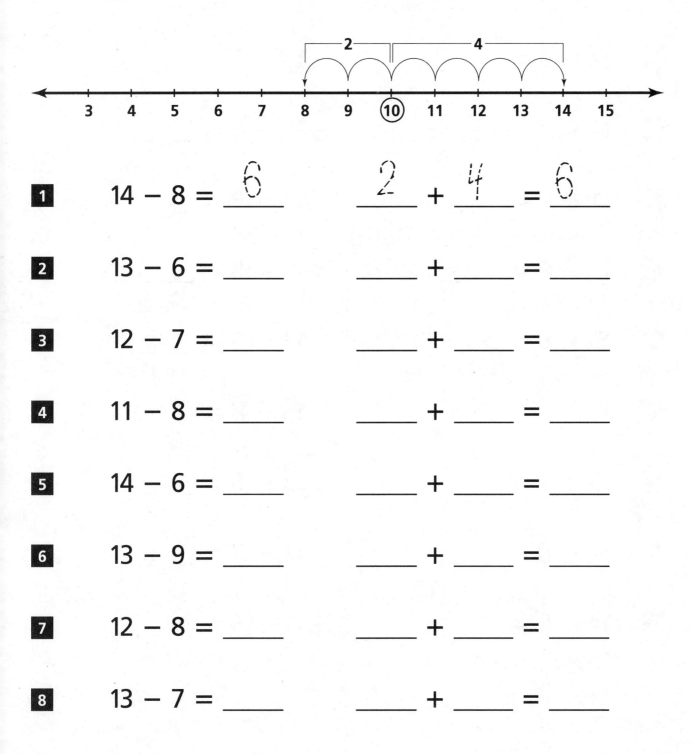

1   14 − 8 = _6_   _2_ + _4_ = _6_

2   13 − 6 = ___   ___ + ___ = ___

3   12 − 7 = ___   ___ + ___ = ___

4   11 − 8 = ___   ___ + ___ = ___

5   14 − 6 = ___   ___ + ___ = ___

6   13 − 9 = ___   ___ + ___ = ___

7   12 − 8 = ___   ___ + ___ = ___

8   13 − 7 = ___   ___ + ___ = ___

$$\xleftarrow{\quad\underset{6}{|}\quad\underset{7}{|}\quad\underset{8}{|}\quad\underset{9}{|}\quad\underset{\textcircled{10}}{|}\quad\underset{11}{|}\quad\underset{12}{|}\quad\underset{13}{|}\quad\underset{14}{|}\quad\underset{15}{|}\quad}\xrightarrow{}$$

Use the 10 between two numbers in a subtraction fact.
Find the difference.

1 $12 - 9 =$ _____ $13 - 7 =$ _____

2 $14 - 7 =$ _____ $11 - 8 =$ _____

3 $11 - 9 =$ _____ $13 - 9 =$ _____

4 $14 - 6 =$ _____ $12 - 8 =$ _____

5 $13 - 8 =$ _____ $12 - 6 =$ _____

6 $11 - 7 =$ _____ $15 - 8 =$ _____

7 $15 - 9 =$ _____ $13 - 6 =$ _____

8 $14 - 8 =$ _____ $12 - 7 =$ _____

9 $14 - 9 =$ _____ $11 - 6 =$ _____

Subtract. Use the 10 between two numbers in a subtraction fact.

1 $13 - 10 =$ _____ $10 - 6 =$ _____ $13 - 6 =$ _____

2 $14 - 10 =$ _____ $10 - 9 =$ _____ $14 - 9 =$ _____

3 $12 - 10 =$ _____ $10 - 8 =$ _____ $12 - 8 =$ _____

4 $13 - 10 =$ _____ $10 - 9 =$ _____ $13 - 9 =$ _____

5 $11 - 10 =$ _____ $10 - 8 =$ _____ $11 - 8 =$ _____

6 $13 - 10 =$ _____ $10 - 7 =$ _____ $13 - 7 =$ _____

Subtract. Draw lines to match same difference.

A

11 – 7 = _____ (A)

14 – 5 = _____ (B)

13 – 8 = _____ (C)

11 – 8 = _____ (D)

12 – 6 = _____ (E)

11 – 10 = _____ (F)

14 – 4 = _____ (G)

13 – 6 = _____ (H)

11 – 9 = _____ (I)

14 – 6 = _____ (J)

B

(1) 12 – 7 = _____

(2) 16 – 6 = _____

(3) 10 – 9 = _____

(4) 12 – 10 = _____

(5) 13 – 5 = _____

(6) 12 – 8 = _____

(7) 12 – 5 = _____

(8) 15 – 6 = _____

(9) 14 – 8 = _____

(10) 12 – 9 = _____

Subtract.

1

13	14	12	11	13
− 6	− 9	− 7	− 8	− 9

2

12	11	14	13	12
− 8	− 9	− 6	− 8	− 6

3

14	13	12	11	14
− 8	− 7	− 9	− 7	− 7

4   11 − 6 = _____   14 − 8 = _____   12 − 6 = _____

5   12 − 7 = _____   11 − 9 = _____   13 − 7 = _____

6   12 − 9 = _____   14 − 7 = _____   11 − 7 = _____

Subtract. Draw lines to match same difference.

A

12 – 9 = _____ Ⓐ

13 – 7 = _____ Ⓑ

14 – 6 = _____ Ⓒ

11 – 9 = _____ Ⓓ

11 – 10 = _____ Ⓔ

12 – 3 = _____ Ⓕ

12 – 8 = _____ Ⓖ

13 – 8 = _____ Ⓗ

14 – 4 = _____ Ⓘ

13 – 6 = _____ Ⓙ

B

① 14 – 9 = _____

② 11 – 7 = _____

③ 12 – 10 = _____

④ 12 – 6 = _____

⑤ 13 – 3 = _____

⑥ 14 – 7 = _____

⑦ 11 – 8 = _____

⑧ 10 – 9 = _____

⑨ 13 – 5 = _____

⑩ 15 – 6 = _____

Subtract. Write the difference.

1

17	14	16	15
− 8	− 6	− 8	− 6

2

11	10	13	12
− 2	− 3	− 5	− 4

3

11	17	10	16
− 4	− 9	− 2	− 9

4

15	14	14	14
− 0	− 5	− 8	− 7

5

13	12	12	13
− 6	− 5	− 6	− 7

Subtract. Write the difference.

1   18 − 8 = _____   16 − 7 = _____   15 − 5 = _____

2   13 − 3 = _____   16 − 6 = _____   14 − 9 = _____

3   18 − 9 = _____   10 − 8 = _____   12 − 7 = _____

4   13 − 4 = _____   11 − 5 = _____   12 − 8 = _____

5   15 − 8 = _____   17 − 7 = _____   10 − 4 = _____

6   12 − 3 = _____   12 − 9 = _____   13 − 4 = _____

Subtract. Write the difference.

1
| 12 | 14 | 16 | 15 |
| − 2 | − 5 | − 7 | − 9 |

2
| 10 | 11 | 13 | 10 |
| − 7 | − 6 | − 8 | − 6 |

3
| 13 | 14 | 17 | 15 |
| − 5 | − 6 | − 8 | − 7 |

4 $12 - 4 =$ _____ $10 - 5 =$ _____ $12 - 7 =$ _____

5 $14 - 8 =$ _____ $15 - 6 =$ _____ $15 - 7 =$ _____

6 $16 - 9 =$ _____ $13 - 9 =$ _____ $12 - 6 =$ _____

Find each difference.
Write the letter on the blank over the differences below.

A. 14 − 9 = _____   K. 13 − 7 = _____

E. 10 − 9 = _____   Y. 11 − 9 = _____

P. 14 − 7 = _____   Q. 15 − 6 = _____

M. 12 − 9 = _____   U. 14 − 6 = _____

C. 13 − 9 = _____   O. 10 − 0 = _____

What did the duck say after
laughing for 10 minutes?

___ ___ ___   ___ ___ ___ ___ ___   ___ ___ ___ ___ !
 2 10 8   9 8 5 4 6   3 1   8 7

Subtract. Write the difference.

1

12	11	13	11
− 3	− 7	− 4	− 8

2

16	13	10	11
− 8	− 6	− 6	− 9

3

13	12	11	17
− 7	− 5	− 3	− 9

4

11	18	15	14
− 4	− 9	− 8	− 7

5

11	12	13	12
− 5	− 8	− 5	− 4

Subtract. Write the difference.

1   13 − 8 = _____   14 − 5 = _____

2   15 − 6 = _____   15 − 7 = _____

3   13 − 6 = _____   12 − 5 = _____

4   14 − 9 = _____   11 − 4 = _____

5   11 − 3 = _____   12 − 2 = _____

6   16 − 7 = _____   14 − 6 = _____

7   14 − 8 = _____   19 − 9 = _____

8   11 − 5 = _____   13 − 4 = _____

9   11 − 7 = _____   13 − 7 = _____

10 12 − 9 = _____   17 − 8 = _____

Subtract. Write the difference.

1

11	12	14	17
− 6	− 6	− 7	− 9

2

11	18	12	15
− 3	− 9	− 8	− 6

3

11	16	16	13
− 9	− 7	− 9	− 8

4   15 − 9 = _____   16 − 8 = _____   12 − 3 = _____

5   13 − 9 = _____   12 − 7 = _____   14 − 9 = _____

6   11 − 8 = _____   14 − 6 = _____   15 − 8 = _____

Subtract. Look for patterns.

1

14	14	14	14	14
− 9	− 8	− 7	− 6	− 5

2

18	17	16	15	14
− 9	− 9	− 9	− 9	− 9

3

11	12	13	14	15
− 4	− 5	− 6	− 7	− 8

4

10	10	10	10	10
− 1	− 2	− 3	− 4	− 5

5

3	4	5	6	7
− 2	− 2	− 2	− 2	− 2

Multiply.

1   2 × 1 = _____   2 × 0 = _____   2 × 10 = _____

2   5 × 1 = _____   5 × 0 = _____   5 × 10 = _____

3   3 × 1 = _____   3 × 0 = _____   3 × 10 = _____

4   7 × 1 = _____   7 × 0 = _____   7 × 10 = _____

5   4 × 1 = _____   4 × 0 = _____   4 × 10 = _____

6   6 × 1 = _____   6 × 0 = _____   6 × 10 = _____

Find the product.

1 $3 \times 0 =$ _____ $1 \times 7 =$ _____ $3 \times 10 =$ _____

2 $1 \times 1 =$ _____ $9 \times 10 =$ _____ $0 \times 2 =$ _____

3 $2 \times 10 =$ _____ $0 \times 4 =$ _____ $6 \times 1 =$ _____

4 $5 \times 10 =$ _____ $2 \times 1 =$ _____ $10 \times 8 =$ _____

5 $1 \times 8 =$ _____ $8 \times 0 =$ _____ $1 \times 10 =$ _____

6 $10 \times 10 =$ _____ $10 \times 4 =$ _____ $9 \times 1 =$ _____

Multiply.

1

8 × 1	2 × 10	7 × 1	8 × 10	5 × 0

2

6 × 10	4 × 0	1 × 2	0 × 1	9 × 1

3

10 × 0	10 × 9	10 × 7	2 × 0	1 × 4

4

10 × 5	10 × 1	10 × 10	6 × 1	9 × 0

5

3 × 1	3 × 10	0 × 3	6 × 0	4 × 10

Find the product.

1 3 × 1 = _____   10 × 1 = _____   5 × 10 = _____

2 9 × 1 = _____   0 × 9 = _____   2 × 0 = _____

3 0 × 7 = _____   7 × 1 = _____   1 × 5 = _____

4
$$\begin{array}{r} 8 \\ \times\, 10 \\ \hline \end{array} \qquad \begin{array}{r} 1 \\ \times\, 2 \\ \hline \end{array} \qquad \begin{array}{r} 0 \\ \times\, 5 \\ \hline \end{array} \qquad \begin{array}{r} 1 \\ \times\, 6 \\ \hline \end{array} \qquad \begin{array}{r} 10 \\ \times\, 10 \\ \hline \end{array}$$

5
$$\begin{array}{r} 10 \\ \times\, 6 \\ \hline \end{array} \qquad \begin{array}{r} 4 \\ \times\, 0 \\ \hline \end{array} \qquad \begin{array}{r} 0 \\ \times\, 8 \\ \hline \end{array} \qquad \begin{array}{r} 2 \\ \times\, 10 \\ \hline \end{array} \qquad \begin{array}{r} 4 \\ \times\, 1 \\ \hline \end{array}$$

6
$$\begin{array}{r} 1 \\ \times\, 1 \\ \hline \end{array} \qquad \begin{array}{r} 7 \\ \times\, 10 \\ \hline \end{array} \qquad \begin{array}{r} 10 \\ \times\, 4 \\ \hline \end{array} \qquad \begin{array}{r} 1 \\ \times\, 8 \\ \hline \end{array} \qquad \begin{array}{r} 9 \\ \times\, 10 \\ \hline \end{array}$$

Multiply.

1. 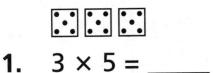 3 × 5 = _____   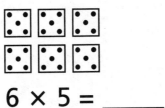 6 × 5 = _____   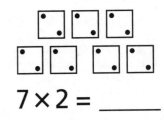 7 × 2 = _____

2. 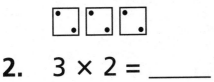 3 × 2 = _____   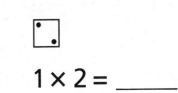 6 × 2 = _____   1 × 2 = _____

3. 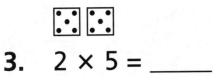 2 × 5 = _____   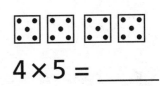 5 × 5 = _____   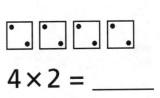 4 × 5 = _____

4. 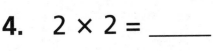 2 × 2 = _____   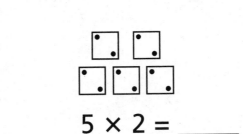 5 × 2 = _____   4 × 2 = _____

5. 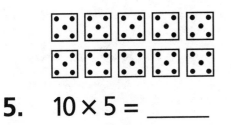 10 × 5 = _____   1 × 5 = _____   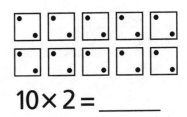 10 × 2 = _____

Multiply.

1 $7 \times 2 =$ _____ $6 \times 2 =$ _____ $1 \times 2 =$ _____

2 $5 \times 3 =$ _____ $8 \times 5 =$ _____ $4 \times 5 =$ _____

3 $2 \times 5 =$ _____ $1 \times 5 =$ _____ $7 \times 5 =$ _____

4 $9 \times 5 =$ _____ $0 \times 5 =$ _____ $2 \times 9 =$ _____

5 $2 \times 3 =$ _____ $8 \times 2 =$ _____ $6 \times 5 =$ _____

6 $0 \times 2 =$ _____ $5 \times 7 =$ _____ $4 \times 2 =$ _____

Multiply.

1
$$
\begin{array}{r} 5 \\ \times\, 3 \\ \hline \end{array}
\qquad
\begin{array}{r} 2 \\ \times\, 2 \\ \hline \end{array}
\qquad
\begin{array}{r} 4 \\ \times\, 5 \\ \hline \end{array}
\qquad
\begin{array}{r} 2 \\ \times\, 3 \\ \hline \end{array}
\qquad
\begin{array}{r} 7 \\ \times\, 2 \\ \hline \end{array}
$$

2
$$
\begin{array}{r} 2 \\ \times\, 9 \\ \hline \end{array}
\qquad
\begin{array}{r} 5 \\ \times\, 6 \\ \hline \end{array}
\qquad
\begin{array}{r} 2 \\ \times\, 4 \\ \hline \end{array}
\qquad
\begin{array}{r} 10 \\ \times\, 2 \\ \hline \end{array}
\qquad
\begin{array}{r} 5 \\ \times\, 2 \\ \hline \end{array}
$$

3
$$
\begin{array}{r} 9 \\ \times\, 5 \\ \hline \end{array}
\qquad
\begin{array}{r} 5 \\ \times\, 1 \\ \hline \end{array}
\qquad
\begin{array}{r} 1 \\ \times\, 2 \\ \hline \end{array}
\qquad
\begin{array}{r} 8 \\ \times\, 2 \\ \hline \end{array}
\qquad
\begin{array}{r} 5 \\ \times\, 0 \\ \hline \end{array}
$$

4
$$
\begin{array}{r} 6 \\ \times\, 2 \\ \hline \end{array}
\qquad
\begin{array}{r} 5 \\ \times\, 5 \\ \hline \end{array}
\qquad
\begin{array}{r} 8 \\ \times\, 5 \\ \hline \end{array}
\qquad
\begin{array}{r} 3 \\ \times\, 2 \\ \hline \end{array}
\qquad
\begin{array}{r} 5 \\ \times\, 10 \\ \hline \end{array}
$$

5
$$
\begin{array}{r} 5 \\ \times\, 8 \\ \hline \end{array}
\qquad
\begin{array}{r} 2 \\ \times\, 0 \\ \hline \end{array}
\qquad
\begin{array}{r} 7 \\ \times\, 5 \\ \hline \end{array}
\qquad
\begin{array}{r} 2 \\ \times\, 2 \\ \hline \end{array}
\qquad
\begin{array}{r} 5 \\ \times\, 3 \\ \hline \end{array}
$$

Color these products red: 5, 10, 15, 20, 25, 30, 35, 40, 45, 50.
Color these products blue: 2, 4, 6, 8, 10, 12, 14, 16, 18, 20.
How many "purple" boxes? _____

1 6 × 5	8 × 2	1 × 5	2 × 2
2 7 × 5	10 × 2	5 × 9	2 × 9
3 4 × 5	0 × 5	5 × 5	2 × 1
4 6 × 2	2 × 5	5 × 8	4 × 2
5 10 × 5	2 × 3	3 × 5	2 × 7

Add.

1 $5 + 1 =$ _____ $2 + 2 =$ _____ $3 + 7 =$ _____

2 $8 + 7 =$ _____ $6 + 5 =$ _____ $0 + 5 =$ _____

Subtract.

3 $10 - 3 =$ _____ $4 - 2 =$ _____ $7 - 1 =$ _____

4 $9 - 5 =$ _____ $8 - 4 =$ _____ $12 - 4 =$ _____

Multiply.

5 $6 \times 1 =$ _____ $4 \times 2 =$ _____ $3 \times 0 =$ _____

6 $4 \times 10 =$ _____ $3 \times 5 =$ _____ $1 \times 1 =$ _____

Look and solve.

1 $\begin{array}{r} 9 \\ +\,5 \\ \hline \end{array}$	$\begin{array}{r} 4 \\ +\,7 \\ \hline \end{array}$	$\begin{array}{r} 2 \\ +\,8 \\ \hline \end{array}$	$\begin{array}{r} 6 \\ +\,3 \\ \hline \end{array}$
2 $\begin{array}{r} 10 \\ -\,7 \\ \hline \end{array}$	$\begin{array}{r} 12 \\ -\,2 \\ \hline \end{array}$	$\begin{array}{r} 18 \\ -\,9 \\ \hline \end{array}$	$\begin{array}{r} 8 \\ -\,2 \\ \hline \end{array}$
3 $\begin{array}{r} 5 \\ \times\,10 \\ \hline \end{array}$	$\begin{array}{r} 2 \\ \times\,5 \\ \hline \end{array}$	$\begin{array}{r} 6 \\ \times\,2 \\ \hline \end{array}$	$\begin{array}{r} 1 \\ \times\,3 \\ \hline \end{array}$
4 $\begin{array}{r} 7 \\ +\,2 \\ \hline \end{array}$	$\begin{array}{r} 7 \\ \times\,2 \\ \hline \end{array}$	$\begin{array}{r} 7 \\ -\,2 \\ \hline \end{array}$	$\begin{array}{r} 4 \\ \times\,10 \\ \hline \end{array}$

Look and solve.

1 $7 + 2 =$ _____ $8 + 1 =$ _____ $4 + 2 =$ _____

2 $9 + 1 =$ _____ $5 + 5 =$ _____ $6 + 5 =$ _____

3 $10 - 9 =$ _____ $9 - 8 =$ _____ $8 - 6 =$ _____

4 $7 - 3 =$ _____ $6 - 1 =$ _____ $4 - 0 =$ _____

5 $4 \times 0 =$ _____ $3 \times 1 =$ _____ $2 \times 10 =$ _____

6 $7 \times 2 =$ _____ $6 \times 5 =$ _____ $3 \times 2 =$ _____

Look and solve.

1

$$\begin{array}{r} 5 \\ + 5 \\ \hline \end{array}$$
$$\begin{array}{r} 6 \\ + 2 \\ \hline \end{array}$$
$$\begin{array}{r} 9 \\ + 3 \\ \hline \end{array}$$
$$\begin{array}{r} 10 \\ + 5 \\ \hline \end{array}$$
$$\begin{array}{r} 7 \\ + 8 \\ \hline \end{array}$$

2

$$\begin{array}{r} 10 \\ - 7 \\ \hline \end{array}$$
$$\begin{array}{r} 17 \\ - 8 \\ \hline \end{array}$$
$$\begin{array}{r} 6 \\ - 3 \\ \hline \end{array}$$
$$\begin{array}{r} 9 \\ - 2 \\ \hline \end{array}$$
$$\begin{array}{r} 10 \\ - 5 \\ \hline \end{array}$$

3

$$\begin{array}{r} 8 \\ - 1 \\ \hline \end{array}$$
$$\begin{array}{r} 12 \\ - 6 \\ \hline \end{array}$$
$$\begin{array}{r} 9 \\ - 7 \\ \hline \end{array}$$
$$\begin{array}{r} 14 \\ - 5 \\ \hline \end{array}$$
$$\begin{array}{r} 18 \\ - 9 \\ \hline \end{array}$$

4

$$\begin{array}{r} 3 \\ \times 10 \\ \hline \end{array}$$
$$\begin{array}{r} 9 \\ \times 1 \\ \hline \end{array}$$
$$\begin{array}{r} 4 \\ \times 10 \\ \hline \end{array}$$
$$\begin{array}{r} 8 \\ \times 2 \\ \hline \end{array}$$
$$\begin{array}{r} 5 \\ \times 2 \\ \hline \end{array}$$

5

$$\begin{array}{r} 9 \\ \times 5 \\ \hline \end{array}$$
$$\begin{array}{r} 1 \\ \times 10 \\ \hline \end{array}$$
$$\begin{array}{r} 0 \\ \times 0 \\ \hline \end{array}$$
$$\begin{array}{r} 4 \\ \times 5 \\ \hline \end{array}$$
$$\begin{array}{r} 8 \\ \times 0 \\ \hline \end{array}$$

Look and solve.

1

$$9 + 1$$ $$8 + 1$$ $$7 + 1$$ $$6 + 1$$ $$5 + 1$$

2

$$18 - 9$$ $$17 - 9$$ $$16 - 9$$ $$15 - 9$$ $$14 - 9$$

3

$$5 \times 2$$ $$5 \times 3$$ $$5 \times 4$$ $$5 \times 5$$ $$5 \times 6$$

4 $3 \times 10 =$ _____ $4 \times 10 =$ _____ $5 \times 10 =$ _____

5 $6 \times 2 =$ _____ $6 \times 1 =$ _____ $6 \times 0 =$ _____

6 $2 + 2 =$ _____ $2 - 2 =$ _____ $2 \times 2 =$ _____

Look and solve.

1	$\begin{array}{r} 4 \\ +\ 6 \\ \hline \end{array}$	$\begin{array}{r} 12 \\ -\ 7 \\ \hline \end{array}$	$\begin{array}{r} 2 \\ \times\ 9 \\ \hline \end{array}$	$\begin{array}{r} 15 \\ -\ 8 \\ \hline \end{array}$	$\begin{array}{r} 10 \\ \times\ 1 \\ \hline \end{array}$
2	$\begin{array}{r} 6 \\ +\ 3 \\ \hline \end{array}$	$\begin{array}{r} 16 \\ -\ 9 \\ \hline \end{array}$	$\begin{array}{r} 9 \\ +\ 5 \\ \hline \end{array}$	$\begin{array}{r} 18 \\ -\ 8 \\ \hline \end{array}$	$\begin{array}{r} 10 \\ -\ 8 \\ \hline \end{array}$
3	$\begin{array}{r} 5 \\ +\ 5 \\ \hline \end{array}$	$\begin{array}{r} 17 \\ -\ 8 \\ \hline \end{array}$	$\begin{array}{r} 7 \\ \times\ 2 \\ \hline \end{array}$	$\begin{array}{r} 10 \\ -\ 5 \\ \hline \end{array}$	$\begin{array}{r} 9 \\ \times\ 2 \\ \hline \end{array}$
4	$\begin{array}{r} 7 \\ \times\ 0 \\ \hline \end{array}$	$\begin{array}{r} 14 \\ \times\ 1 \\ \hline \end{array}$	$\begin{array}{r} 10 \\ +\ 3 \\ \hline \end{array}$	$\begin{array}{r} 2 \\ \times\ 5 \\ \hline \end{array}$	$\begin{array}{r} 10 \\ \times\ 1 \\ \hline \end{array}$
5	$\begin{array}{r} 10 \\ +\ 2 \\ \hline \end{array}$	$\begin{array}{r} 14 \\ -\ 4 \\ \hline \end{array}$	$\begin{array}{r} 5 \\ \times\ 3 \\ \hline \end{array}$	$\begin{array}{r} 18 \\ -\ 9 \\ \hline \end{array}$	$\begin{array}{r} 0 \\ +\ 10 \\ \hline \end{array}$

Look and solve.

1 $10 - 1 =$ _____ $5 \times 10 =$ _____ $5 + 0 =$ _____

2 $4 \times 2 =$ _____ $10 + 7 =$ _____ $14 - 7 =$ _____

3 $8 + 9 =$ _____ $8 - 7 =$ _____ $7 \times 1 =$ _____

4 $3 \times 5 =$ _____ $4 + 1 =$ _____ $8 - 2 =$ _____

5 $2 + 2 =$ _____ $9 - 6 =$ _____ $7 \times 5 =$ _____

6 $10 - 6 =$ _____ $6 \times 0 =$ _____ $3 + 6 =$ _____

Look and solve.

1

$$
\begin{array}{r} 9 \\ -\ 1 \\ \hline \end{array}
\qquad
\begin{array}{r} 9 \\ +\ 2 \\ \hline \end{array}
\qquad
\begin{array}{r} 4 \\ \times\ 10 \\ \hline \end{array}
\qquad
\begin{array}{r} 17 \\ -\ 8 \\ \hline \end{array}
\qquad
\begin{array}{r} 1 \\ +\ 3 \\ \hline \end{array}
$$

2

$$
\begin{array}{r} 5 \\ +\ 9 \\ \hline \end{array}
\qquad
\begin{array}{r} 5 \\ \times\ 9 \\ \hline \end{array}
\qquad
\begin{array}{r} 4 \\ +\ 4 \\ \hline \end{array}
\qquad
\begin{array}{r} 3 \\ \times\ 0 \\ \hline \end{array}
\qquad
\begin{array}{r} 8 \\ -\ 3 \\ \hline \end{array}
$$

3

$$
\begin{array}{r} 4 \\ +\ 7 \\ \hline \end{array}
\qquad
\begin{array}{r} 7 \\ -\ 2 \\ \hline \end{array}
\qquad
\begin{array}{r} 7 \\ \times\ 2 \\ \hline \end{array}
\qquad
\begin{array}{r} 10 \\ +\ 2 \\ \hline \end{array}
\qquad
\begin{array}{r} 7 \\ \times\ 5 \\ \hline \end{array}
$$

4

$$
\begin{array}{r} 3 \\ -\ 0 \\ \hline \end{array}
\qquad
\begin{array}{r} 3 \\ \times\ 1 \\ \hline \end{array}
\qquad
\begin{array}{r} 8 \\ +\ 3 \\ \hline \end{array}
\qquad
\begin{array}{r} 1 \\ \times\ 10 \\ \hline \end{array}
\qquad
\begin{array}{r} 9 \\ -\ 9 \\ \hline \end{array}
$$

5

$$
\begin{array}{r} 8 \\ +\ 9 \\ \hline \end{array}
\qquad
\begin{array}{r} 4 \\ -\ 4 \\ \hline \end{array}
\qquad
\begin{array}{r} 5 \\ \times\ 3 \\ \hline \end{array}
\qquad
\begin{array}{r} 7 \\ +\ 6 \\ \hline \end{array}
\qquad
\begin{array}{r} 0 \\ \times\ 10 \\ \hline \end{array}
$$

Complete.
Color boxes with even answers blue.
Color boxes with odd answers yellow.

1			
10 − 4	7 + 10	9 + 5	5 × 5
2			
8 − 7	6 × 2	14 − 5	6 + 4
3			
3 × 10	12 − 9	7 + 7	7 − 0
4			
5 + 0	0 × 5	4 − 1	8 + 2
5			
9 + 9	3 × 3	5 × 10	11 − 6

Look and solve.

1

7	3	10	10	7
+ 3	+ 7	− 7	− 3	× 10

2

3	5	2	5	2
+ 2	− 2	+ 3	− 3	× 5

3

6	1	7	7	1
+ 1	+ 6	− 1	− 6	× 6

4 $4 + 5 =$ _____ $5 + 4 =$ _____ $8 - 3 =$ _____

5 $8 - 5 =$ _____ $5 \times 2 =$ _____ $2 \times 5 =$ _____

6 $7 + 6 =$ _____ $6 + 7 =$ _____ $14 - 9 =$ _____

Color products: 0 to 25 orange   26 to 90 green

Color sums: 0 to 9 red   10 to 18 blue

Color differences: 0 to 5 yellow   6 to 9 purple

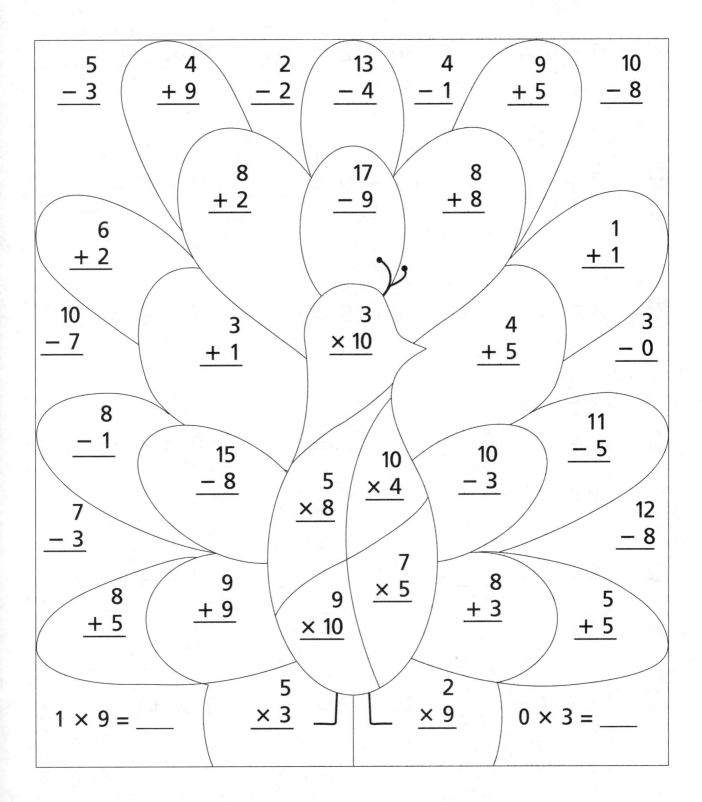

Look and solve.

1 10 + 2 = _____   10 − 2 = _____   10 × 2 = _____

2 2 + 0 = _____   2 − 0 = _____   0 × 2 = _____

3 8 + 5 = _____   8 − 5 = _____   5 × 8 = _____

4 6 + 0 = _____   6 − 0 = _____   0 × 6 = _____

5 4 + 2 = _____   4 − 2 = _____   2 × 4 = _____

6 10 + 7 = _____   10 − 7 = _____   7 × 10 = _____